Secondary Certificate

Mathematics ANSWERS

Second edition
Revised and metricated

D. T. DANIEL, B.A., Dip. Ed.

Head of Mathematics Dept., Lancastrian Boys' School
Formerly Head of Mathematics, The Weald School

NELSON

THOMAS NELSON AND SONS LTD
36 Park Street London W1Y 4DE
P.O Box 18123 Nairobi
P.O. Box 21149 Dar es Salaam
P.O. Box 2187 Accra
77 Coffee Street San Fernando Trinidad

THOMAS NELSON (AUSTRALIA) LTD
597 Little Collins Street Melbourne 3000

THOMAS NELSON AND SONS (SOUTH AFRICA) (PROPRIETARY) LTD
51 Commissioner Street Johannesburg

THOMAS NELSON AND SONS (CANADA) LTD
81 Curlew Drive Don Mills Ontario

THOMAS NELSON (NIGERIA) LTD
P.O. Box 336 Apapa Lagos

First published 1965
Second edition, revised and metricated, 1970

17 431004 8

Made and printed by offset in Great Britain by
William Clowes and Sons, Limited, London and Beccles

PART ONE—ARITHMETIC

1 The Four Rules

Exercise 1   Page 1

1	*(a)* 431	*(b)* 1,054	*(c)* 3,620	
2	*(a)* 9,823	*(b)* 1,750	*(c)* 2,920	
3	*(a)* 8,212	*(b)* 5,680	*(c)* 68,948	*(d)* 18,353
4	*(a)* 153	*(b)* 328	*(c)* 49	
5	*(a)* 227	*(b)* 472	*(c)* 2,747	
6	*(a)* 457	*(b)* 1,079	*(c)* 398	*(d)* 2,406

7   *(a)* 1,136   *(c)* 12,339   *(e)* 220,779
    (b) 4,284   *(d)* 12,502   *(f)* 413,440

8 *(a)* 10,512   *(b)* 43,092   *(c)* 76,832   *(d)* 448,812

9 *(a)* 218   *(e)* 17 rem. 17 *(i)* 5 rem. 38
   (b) 35   *(f)* 193 rem. 8 *(j)* 173 rem. 194
   (c) 30 rem. 12 *(g)* 52 rem. 92 *(k)* 11
   (d) 367   *(h)* 73 rem. 26 *(l)* 531

10 *(a)* 72   *(b)* $\frac{46}{81}$ *(c)* $39\frac{3}{5}$ *(d)* 91

11 *(a)* 158   *(b)* 19   *(c)* 4   *(d)* 221

12 *(a)* 4   *(b)* 2   *(c)* $3\frac{45}{46}$ *(d)* 22

Exercise 2 Page 10

1

	(i)	(ii)	(iii)	(iv)	(v)
(a)	111_5	1000_5	304_5	1231_5	3201_5
(b)	37_8	175_8	117_8	277_8	652_8
(c)	27_{12}	$T5_{12}$	67_{12}	$13E_{12}$	$2E6_{12}$
(d)	11111_2	1111101_2	1001111_2	101111111_2	110101010_2

2 28, 273, 23, 127, 53, 238,
   279, 48, 21, 97

3

	Base 10	Base 8	Base 5	Base 12	Base 2
(i)	24	30	44	20	11000
(ii)	17	21	32	15	10001
(iii)	18	22	33	16	10010
(iv)	136	210	1021	E4	10001000
(v)	43	53	83	37	101011

4 *(a)* 1232_5 *(c)* 1317_8 *(e)* 532_6 *(g)* 110001_2
   (b) 1586_{12} *(d)* 100000_2 *(f)* 816_{12} *(h)* 1011000_2

5 (a) 124_8 (c) 343_{12} (e) 156_7 (g) 101101_2
   (b) 44_5 (d) 100_2 (f) $ITE6_{12}$ (h) 10000110_2
6 (a) 1442_5 (b) 4302_8 (c) $6E9_{12}$ (d) 1000001_2
   (e) 20413_5 (f) 33105_6 (g) 16630_{12} (h) 1111110_2
   (i) 11010101111_2
7 (a) 41_5 (b) 11_8 rem. 23_8 (c) 507_{12} rem. 14_{12}
   (d) 101_2 rem. 10_2 (e) 3_4 rem. 110_4 (f) $3T_{12}$ rem. 92_{12}
   (g) 4_8 rem. 157_8 (h) 1011_2 rem. 11_2
8 (a) Correct, Base 8   (b) Correct, Base 5   (c) Wrong,
   (d) Wrong, Base 10   (e) Correct, Base 4   Base 8
9 (a) 132_8 (b) 101111110_2 (c) $20T3_{12}$ (d) 111110100_2
   (e) 664_8
10 16 symbols, $4V_{16}$ and $6U_{16}$ (where V $= 15_{10}$ and U $= 13_{10}$)

2 Vulgar Fractions

Exercise 1   Pages 15 and 17

1	$5\frac{9}{16}$	**10**	$24\frac{3}{16}$	**18**	1	**26**	$1\frac{1}{2}$
2	$9\frac{13}{40}$	**11**	$13\frac{3}{5}$	**19**	$4\frac{1}{4}$	**27**	$\frac{4}{5}$
3	$2\frac{7}{16}$	**12**	$9\frac{69}{128}$	**20**	10	**28**	$3\frac{1}{2}$
4	$6\frac{2}{3}$	**13**	$3\frac{3}{20}$	**21**	$4\frac{17}{18}$	**29**	$\frac{9}{25}$
5	$3\frac{4}{5}$	**14**	$\frac{7}{25}$	**22**	$14\frac{2}{3}$	**30**	$2\frac{2}{3}$
6	$4\frac{19}{24}$	**15**	$4\frac{4}{9}$	**23**	$5\frac{3}{32}$	**31**	$\frac{176}{441}$
7	$2\frac{31}{32}$	**16**	$8\frac{1}{8}$	**24**	$2\frac{2}{33}$	**32**	$\frac{5}{16}$
8	$2\frac{7}{8}$	**17**	2	**25**	$1\frac{1}{2}$	**33**	$\frac{7}{243}$
9	$1\frac{31}{32}$						

Exercise 2   Page 19

1 (a) $\frac{1}{8}$ (b) $\frac{2}{25}$ **2** (a) $\frac{3}{16}$ (b) $\frac{1}{4}$ **3** 42p, £3·25$\frac{1}{2}$
4 $\frac{9}{20}$, 126·5 litres   **5** 17·2 metres   **6** $\frac{3}{28}$
7 170   **8** 32 strips   **9** Copper 405 g, Tin 31·5 g, Zinc 13·5 g
10 72 km

Exercise 3   Page 23

1 (a) $\frac{7}{8}$ (b) $\frac{4}{5}$ (c) $\frac{8}{9}$
2 $\frac{1}{4}, \frac{1}{3}, \frac{1}{2}, \frac{2}{3}, \frac{3}{4}$. Order 4
3 $\frac{1}{6}, \frac{1}{5}, \frac{1}{4}, \frac{1}{3}, \frac{2}{5}, \frac{1}{2}, \frac{3}{5}, \frac{2}{3}, \frac{3}{4}, \frac{4}{5}, \frac{5}{6}$
4 (a) Yes   (b) No   (c) Yes   (d) Yes   (e) No
5 (a) $\frac{1}{4}$ (b) $\frac{2}{3}$ (c) $\frac{4}{5}$
6 $\frac{1}{8}, \frac{1}{7}, \frac{1}{6}, \frac{1}{5}, \frac{1}{4}, \frac{2}{7}, \frac{1}{3}, \frac{3}{8}, \frac{2}{5}, \frac{3}{7}, \frac{1}{2}, \frac{4}{7}, \frac{3}{5}, \frac{5}{8}, \frac{2}{3}, \frac{5}{7}, \frac{3}{4}, \frac{4}{5}, \frac{5}{6}, \frac{6}{7}, \frac{7}{8}$
7 $\frac{17}{31}$ **8** $\frac{3}{5}$ **9** $\frac{89}{151}$

3 Decimal Fractions

Exercise 1   Page 28

1   *(a)* 3·086   *(c)* 0·375   *(e)* 25·463
    (b) 49·067   *(d)* 1·667   *(f)* 2·071

2 i *(a)* 3   *(c)* 4   *(e)* 7   *(g)* 4
     (b) 4   *(d)* 6   *(f)* 4

  ii *(a)* 5·4   *(c)* 7·9   *(e)* 22   *(g)* 0·057
     (b) 3·5   *(d)* 10   *(f)* 0·0032

3   *(a)* 251·7, 2517   *(e)* 30·25, 302·5   *(i)* 116·63, 1,166·3
    (b) 5·127, 51·27   *(f)* 0·07, 0·7   *(j)* 7, 70
    (c) 50·026, 500·26   *(g)* 120·304, 1,203·04
    (d) 47, 470   *(h)* 0·87, 8·7

4   *(a)* 1·94, 0·194   *(e)* 1·203, 0·1203   *(i)* 3·625, 0·3625
    (b) 0·08, 0·008   *(f)* 7·49, 0·749   *(j)* 80·6002, 8·06002
    (c) 0·003, 0·0003   *(g)* 0·325, 0·0325
    (d) 12·76, 1·276   *(h)* 24, 2·4

5   *(a)* 0·375   *(c)* 1·8   *(e)* 3·4167   *(g)* 0·6875
    (b) 0·8ġ   *(d)* 0·4286   *(f)* 0·9615   *(h)* 0·7458

6   *(a)* $\frac{3}{25}$ *(c)* $5\frac{1}{8}$ *(e)* $7\frac{19}{40}$ *(g)* $\frac{13}{20}$
    (b) $\frac{1}{40}$ *(d)* $\frac{3}{200}$ *(f)* $5\frac{33}{400}$ *(h)* $\frac{7}{200}$

7   *(a)* 103·979   *(c)* 16·564   *(e)* 164·578
    (b) 203·603   *(d)* 205·813

8   *(a)* 0·893   *(b)* 3·07   *(c)* 10·107   *(d)* 5·971   *(e)* 61·086

9   *(a)* 1·68   *(b)* 9·685   *(c)* 21·439   *(d)* 689·185   *(e)* 100·839

10 *(a)* 37·625   *(b)* 77·875   *(c)* 50·225

11 *(a)* 5·6049   *(b)* 747·8538   *(c)* 1,686·2742

12 *(a)* 15   *(b)* 7·5   **14** *(a)* 12·5   *(b)* 800

13 *(a)* 10·08   *(b)* 3·36   **15**   66·24; 6·624; 6,624

16 *(a)* £0·45   *(b)* £3·36   *(c)* £0·64½   *(d)* £0·02½

17 *(a)* 0·333 t   *(b)* 4·265 m³   *(c)* 0·358 m   *(d)* 2·875 km

18 *(a)* 25,000 g *(b)* 36·547 m   *(c)* 0·1545 km *(d)* 35 cm³

19 *(a)* 6½p   *(b)* £4·78½   *(c)* 45p

20 1st by 96 m

4 Metric Weights and Measures

Exercise 1   Page 35

1   *(a)* 4·54 m   *(b)* 454 cm   **2** *(a)* 3·32 km   *(b)* 3,320 m
3   *(a)* 264 cm   *(b)* 2,640 mm **4** *(a)* 4·155 kg *(b)* 4,155 g
5   2·355 l   **6** *(a)* 0·75 m   *(b)* 750 mm

7 (*a*) 4 km 836 m   (*b*) 27 km 40 m   (*c*) 5 km 794m
   (*d*) 33 km 671 m   (*e*) 9 km 450 m
8 (*a*) 12 m 47 cm 3 mm   (*b*) 5 m 90 cm 1 mm
   (*c*) 3 m 48 cm 6 mm   (*d*) 7 m
   (*e*) 2007 m 14 cm   (*f*) 3m 46 cm 2 mm
9 50 cm^3 **10** 0·64 m^2 **11** 500 l   **12** 125 cm^3
13 (*a*) 37·545 m (*b*) 3,754·5 cm **14** (*a*) 1·667 l (*b*) 2·738 kg
15 (*a*) 73·75 m, 177 m, 383·5 m
   (*b*) 15·975 kg, 38·34 kg, 83·07 kg
16 (*a*) 1·775 m   (*b*) 17·75 m   (*c*) 177·5 m
17 (*a*) 20·455 kg   (*b*) 32·85 m   (*c*) 8·75 l
   (*d*) 139 ml   (*e*) 5·65 h   (*f*) 42 h 45 min
   (*g*) 23 h 25 min   (*h*) 3·05 m   (*i*) 6·75 kg
18 2·3 m   **19** 10·6 km/l   **20** (*a*) 0·19125 km (*b*) 3·528 l
21 0·5625 m^2, 900   **22** (*a*) 13·9 m/s (*b*) 50 l/s (*c*) 9·6 ha/8 h
23 2·5 t   **24** 131 l, £8·51½
25 (*a*) 920 g flour, 460 g butter, 460 g sugar
   (*b*) 287·5 g flour, 143·75 g butter, 143·75 g sugar
26 (*a*) 8·33 m/s   (*b*) 60 km/h (to nearest km)
27 (*a*) 1·575 m   (*b*) 1575 mm
28 (*a*) 152 km/h   (*b*) 42·2 m/s   **29** 250 l/m, 4·17 kg
30 10·638 t

5 Money

Exercise 1   Page 39

1 (*a*) £2·00½   (*b*) £46·82   (*c*) £755·64   (*d*) £6·84½
2 (*a*) £8·81   (*b*) £56·69   (*c*) £0·21   (*d*) 0·16½
   (*e*) £48·70
3 (*a*) £9·12   (*b*) £29·12   (*c*) £48·80   (*d*) £348·48
   (*e*) £95·16   (*f*) £24·96
4 (*a*) £0·92   (*b*) £1·41½   (*c*) £0·07 or 7p
   (*d*) £3·68   (*e*) £1·57½   (*f*) £0·56 rem. 20p
5 (*a*) (i) 0·96, $\frac{24}{25}$ (ii) 2·25, $2\frac{1}{4}$ (iii) 4·4, $4\frac{2}{5}$
     (iv) 0·86, $\frac{43}{50}$
   (*b*) (i) 0·192, $\frac{24}{125}$ (ii) 0·45, $\frac{9}{20}$ (iii) 0·88, $\frac{22}{25}$
     (iv) 0·172, $\frac{43}{250}$
6 (*a*) £45·50   (*b*) £10·50   **7** £3·28   **8** 38½p

Exercise 2   Page 41

1 (*a*) 42p   (*b*) 39p   (*c*) 1p   (*d*) 7p   (*e*) 1p
   (*f*) 2p

2 *(a)* In Britain by $6\frac{1}{2}$p   *(b)* In Spain by 7p
   (c) From America by 10p
3 24·30 marks   **4** 85·15 kroner, 27p   **5** 254·25 francs

6 Averages

Exercise 1   Page 44

1 (i) 1·62 m   (ii) 55·77 kg   (iii) 14 yr 3 mths
2 A $-0·1$ m $-8·32$ kg -5 months
    G $-0·15$ m $-12·68$ kg -4 months
    L $+0·105$ m $+8·63$ kg $+5$ months
3 34·125 cm
4 Average £4·19 (to nearest 1p). Type 1, £1·14 below. Type 2,
   $6\frac{1}{2}$p below. Type 3, £0·96 above.
5 69   **6** 46·8 km/h   **7** 179·3 m, 8,965 m   **8** 6p
9 11·1s, 32 km/h   **10** The sister by 19 minutes

7 Ratio and Proportion

Exercise 1   Page 48

1 *(a)* $\frac{1}{20}$ *(b)* $\frac{1}{4}$ *(c)* $\frac{9}{11}$ *(d)* $\frac{1}{4}$ *(e)* $\frac{1}{5}$
2 *(a)* 3:5   *(b)* 3:5   *(c)* 9:25   **3** £60, £80
4 £27, £24, £3   **5** 15 cm, 20 cm, 25 cm
6 (i) 1·333   (ii) 1·667   **7** 37·5 cm
8 *(a)* $\frac{1}{10,000}$ *(b)* $\frac{1}{50,000}$ **9** 9 km
10 $\frac{1}{20,000}$, 62·5 cm
11 *(a)* 1·25 m   *(b)* 2·35 m   *(c)* 42·5 m   *(d)* 3·216 m
12 4:5   **13** 4 pupils   **14** 46 mm   **15** £980
16 £24   **17** Cement 0·8 t, Sand 2 t, Ballast 3·2 t
18 19 m   **19** 67   **20** 480 km, 39 l

8 Percentages

Exercise 1   Page 53

1 *(a)* $\frac{9}{20}$ *(d)* $1\frac{3}{10}$ *(g)* $\frac{1}{8}$ *(j)* $\frac{33}{400}$
   (b) $\frac{7}{10}$ *(e)* $\frac{11}{100}$ *(h)* $\frac{1}{40}$ *(k)* $\frac{2}{3}$
   (c) $\frac{19}{20}$ *(f)* $\frac{57}{100}$ *(i)* $\frac{1}{3}$ *(l)* $\frac{3}{80}$

2   *(a)* 75%   *(d)* $12\frac{1}{2}$%   *(g)* $233\frac{1}{3}$%   *(j)* 85%
     (b) 70%   *(e)* $8\frac{1}{3}$%   *(h)* $462\frac{1}{2}$%   *(k)* $62\frac{1}{2}$%
     (c) 22%   *(f)* 250%   *(i)* 60%   *(l)* $312\frac{1}{2}$%

3   *(a)* 20%   *(b)* 5%   *(c)* $2\frac{1}{2}$%   *(d)* $8\frac{1}{3}$%
     (e) 25%   *(f)* 6%   *(g)* 20%   *(h)* 25%

4   *(a)* £4·05   *(b)* £1·95   *(c)* $59\frac{1}{2}$p   *(d)* 1·1 kg
     (e) 1·92 m   *(f)* £25·39

5   *(a)* £2   *(b)* 2 km   *(c)* 500   *(d)* £1·$87\frac{1}{2}$
     (e) £3,200

6   *(a)* 345   *(b)* £79·20   *(c)* 512·5 g   *(d)* £52·10

7   *(a)* 485   *(b)* 364   *(c)* £69   *(d)* £56·95

8 $11\frac{2}{3}$%   **9** £9·$97\frac{1}{2}$ **10** $18\frac{3}{4}$%   **11** £4·50

12 35   **13** 2·2% approx   **14** 1,600

Exercise 2   Page 57

1   *(a)* Profit 25%   *(b)* Profit 25%   *(c)* Loss$17\frac{7}{9}$%
     (d) Profit $12\frac{1}{2}$%   *(e)* Profit 25%   *(f)* Loss $8\frac{1}{3}$%

2   *(a)* 50%   *(b)* 50%   **3**   *(a)* 19·05%   *(b)* 16%

4 14·71%   **5**   £3·24   **6** 369 m³   **7** £146·25, 36·7%

8 £2·$12\frac{1}{2}$ **9**   30p   **10** £20·25, 7·2%

9 Interest

Exercise 1   Page 60

1   *(a)* £52·50   *(b)* £29·25   *(c)* £5·25

2   *(a)* £1·68   *(b)* £1·71   *(c)* £25·74

3 6%   **4** 6 months   **5** £1,486   **6** £16·56

Exercise 2   Page 62

1 £520·93, £70·93   **6** £231·68, £11·68
2 £303·75, 63·75   **7** £1,130·06, £130·06
3 £1,639·09, £139·09   **8** £46·37, £6·37
4 £751·71, £56·71   **9** £32·71, £2·71
5 £2,483·58, £233·58   **10** £1,040·60, £40·60

Exercise 3   Page 64

1   *(a)* £275·95, to nearest 1p   *(b)* £275·95, to nearest 1p
     (c) £276, to nearest pound

2   £6·40, to nearest 1p

3 *(a)* £395·10, £70·10 *(b)* £220·80, £55·80
   (c) £472·30, £52·30
4 £31, £53 **5** £170

10 Area and Volume

Exercise 1 Page 69

1 *(a)* A 49·5 cm², P 29 cm *(b)* L 20 cm, P 57·5 cm
   (c) A 11·875 m², P 14·5 m *(d)* L 25 cm, A 375 cm²
   (e) B 3·25 m, A 30·875 m² *(f)* B 1·7 m, P 8·4 m
2 *(a)* A 0·018 m² *(b)* A 66·6 cm² *(c)* B 2·5 cm
   (d) H 2·5 cm *(e)* H 7·3 cm
3 25 cm² **4** 9 m
5 (i) 17·5 m² (ii) 58·5 cm² (iii) 46·1 cm² (iv) 36·56 cm²
6 0·805 m² **7** 1,921·875 cm² **8** 66 m², 6 l (5·86)
9 25·42 cm² **10** 362·5 cm²

Exercise 2 Page 75

1 *(a)* 22 cm *(b)* 392·9 mm *(c)* 4·7 m *(d)* 6·6 cm
2 *(a)* 2·2 m *(b)* 22 cm *(c)* 66 cm *(d)* 327 mm
3 *(a)* 0·7 m *(b)* 8 cm *(c)* 4·5 cm *(d)* 4·6 m
4 *(a)* 10·5 cm *(b)* 1·5 mm *(c)* 1·25 cm *(d)* 0·735 m
5 *(a)* 616 cm² *(b)* 38·5 cm² *(c)* 18·1 cm² *(d)* 78·6 m²
6 *(a)* R 2·11 mm *(b)* R 3·5 cm *(c)* R 10·5 cm *(d)* R 1·5 m
   D 4·22 mm D 7 cm D 21 cm D 3 m
7 44 m **8** 5¼ **9** 40,003·6 km **10** 14
11 254·34 cm² **12** 38·5 km²
13 51·9 cm² **14** 8·64 m², 34·5 m **15** 12·68 cm²
16 *(a)* P 44·97 cm *(b)* P 109·9 cm *(c)* P 40·3 cm
   A 120·2 cm² A 137·4 cm² A 44·16 cm²
   (d) P 31·4 cm *(e)* P 3·78 m
   A 21·5 cm² A 0·72 cm²
17 167 cm
18 1,500 mm, 2,100 mm, 444 r.p.m., 317 r.p.m.
19 9,856 cm² **20** 2·21 m **21** 450 m, to nearest metre

Exercise 3 Page 86

1 73·5 cm²

2

	Number of faces	No. of faces of these shapes			
		Square	Rectangle	Triangle	Circle
Rectangular Prism	6		6		
Triangular Prism	5		3	2	
Square Prism	6	2	4		
Cylinder	3		1		2
Pyramid, Sq. base	5	1		4	
Pyramid, Triangular base	4			4	

3   *(a)* 2,500 cm², 8,437·5 cm³   *(b)* 0·18 m², 475 cm³
     (c) 937·5 cm², 750 cm³
4   4,420 litres, 15·85 m²   **5**   59 m²   **6**   7,970 cm³
7   63 m², 135 m³   **8**   526 m³   **9**   238·2 cm
10   0·35 m   **11**   301 l/min   **12**   150 cm², 93·75 cm³
13   40 cm   **14**   4,092 cm³   **15**   169·7 cm²
16   0·519 m²
17   Diam. of sphere, 12·5 cm; vol. of sphere, 1,023 cm³; vol. of cylinder, 1,533 cm³; $\frac{2}{3}$ approx.
18   0·52 m²   **19**   0·09 m³, 5,400 l/h   **20**   91·8 mm

PART TWO—ALGEBRA

11 The Techniques of Algebra

Exercise 1   Page 92

1 Add 7 to $2 \times a$.
2 Take 3 from $5 \times x$.
3 Add a and b, divide the result by 4.
4 Divide 10 by the sum of $2 \times a$, and 3.
5 Take q from $p \times p$ and divide the result by z.
6 Divide a into the sum of $4 \times b + 2$ and take $d \times d$ from this result.

7	14	12	2	17	$2\frac{2}{3}$
8	3	13	$2\frac{5}{6}$	18	$\frac{1}{5}$
9	6	14	$1\frac{7}{9}$	19	$\frac{21}{100}$
10	2	15	15	20	3
11	$\frac{1}{2}$	16	$\frac{1}{8}$		

Exercise 2   Page 95

1 (a) $+3$ (b) $+5$ (c) -3 (d) 0
2 (a) $+6x$ (b) $-5y$ (c) $-8a$ (d) $+5x^2$ (e) $+3-b$
3 (a) $3x+4y$ (b) $3p-8q$ (c) $7t+2$ (d) $6-5a^2$
4 (a) $10a^2+3a-4$ (b) $5x^2+3x-4$ (c) $3q-3p-2p^2$
    (d) $7-3b-b^2$ (e) $10-2a^2$
5 (a) 3   (b) -4 (c) -27 (d) $2x$ (e) $-6a$ (f) $23r^2$
6 (a) 5   (b) 11   (c) -8 (d) $5y$ (e) $-13a^2$ (f) $27a^2b$
7 (a) $x+7y$ (b) $7m+13$ (c) b
    (d) $9z-4$ (e) $3r^2-4s^2$ (f) $-4p^2+4q^2$
8 (a) $2a^2-6a+13$ (b) $12x^2-x-12$ (c) $9y^2-4y-10$
    (d) $-5b^2+7b-20$ (e) $10x^2-18x+34$ (f) $3p^3+5p^2-6p+5$
9 $6a^2-2a-3$ 11 $3x+6y-15z$
10 $2a^2+4a-3b^2$ 12 $2y^2+y+4$

Exercise 3   Page 98

1 (a) -10 (b) -18 (c) 24   (d) 28
    (e) -8 (f) -20 (g) $15x$ (h) $21a$
    (i) $-36a$ (j) $-30y$ (k) $-60p$ (l) $-40k$

2 (a) -2 (b) 3   (c) -5 (d) 2   (e) -2
   (f) -7 (g) 6   (h) -8 (i) -8 (j) 3
   (k) -4 (l) -4 (m) -5

12 Indices or Powers

Exercise 1   Page 99

1 (a) x^5 (b) a^4 (c) $12y^6$ (d) $8b^4$ (e) $-x^5$
   (f) $-a^4$ (g) $2b^5$ (h) $-12m^5$ (i) $-8p^6$
2 (a) a (b) x^3 (c) 3   (d) 2   (e) $-6a$
   (f) $-2x$ (g) $-4z^2$ (h) $3x^2$ (i) $2x$ (j) $3a^2$
   (k) $-4m$ (l) $4k$ (m) $-2x^2$
3 (a) $1\frac{1}{3}$ (b) $2b$ (c) $-3m^4$ (d) $-1\frac{2}{3}$
4 (a) $9a^2$ (b) $18a^4$ (c) $3a^2$ (d) 2

Exercise 2   Page 101

1 (a) $a^3 \times a^3 = a^{3+3} = a^6$
   (b) $2z \times 2z \times 2z = 8z^{1+1+1} = 8z^3$ (c) $\dfrac{c}{4} \times \dfrac{c}{4} = \dfrac{c^2}{16}$
   (d) $(pq)^2 = pq \times pq = p^2q^2$
2 (a) b^6 (b) x^8 (c) $4a^2$ (d) $-x^3$ (e) $9m^2$
   (f) $-8b^6$ (g) a^2b^2 (h) $27x^6y^6$ (i) $16m^4n^2$
3 (a) x (b) b (c) a (d) $2x^2$ (e) $2a^2$
   (f) $4b$ (g) ab (h) $2x^2y^3$ (i) mn^2

Exercise 3   Page 103

1 (a) 3   (b) 2   (c) 5   (d) 2   (e) 6   (f) 4
2 (a) $\sqrt{x}$ (b) $\sqrt[5]{y}$ (c) $\sqrt[3]{a^2}$ (d) $\sqrt[4]{b^3}$ (e) $\sqrt{c^3}$ (f) $\sqrt{m}$
3 (a) $\frac{1}{4}$ (b) $\frac{1}{5}$ (c) $\frac{1}{16}$ (d) $\frac{1}{8}$ (e) 1   (f) $\frac{1}{27}$
   (g) 1
4 (a) $\dfrac{1}{x^3}$ (b) $\dfrac{1}{n^2}$ (c) $\dfrac{1}{b^5}$ (d) $\dfrac{1}{a^4}$
5 (a) 1   (b) 1   (c) 1   (d) 1   (e) 5   (f) 12
6 (a) 3×10^6 (b) 2.75×10^5 (c) 1.8×10^8
   (d) 3.8×10^4
7 (a) 4.6×10^{-4} (b) 9×10^{-6} (c) 3.7×10^{-5}
   (d) 1.56×10^{-5}
8 (a) 1.05×10^{10} (b) 1.65×10^{13} (c) 4×10^{-2}
   (d) 3.6×10^{-2}

Exercise 4　Page 106

1　(a) $8a + 12$　　(b) $12b - 6$　　(c) $10a + 12b$
　　(d) $3p^2 + 6p$　　(e) $3p - 5p^2$　　(f) $-21p^2 - 12pq$
　　(g) $c^3 - 4c^2$　　(h) $4z^2 - 6z^3$　　(i) $12a^2b^2 - 21ab$
　　(j) $24mn - 15m^3n^2$　(k) $10a^3 - 15a^2 + 20a$
　　　　　　　　　　(l) $12ab^2 - 8a^2b - 20a^3$

2　(a) $10a - 15$　(d) $6r^2 + 12r$　(g) $6c^2 - 8c$
　　(b) $21b + 28$　(e) $-12a - 15$　(h) $8b^2 - 4b^3$
　　(c) $12x - 8$　(f) $-24b - 42$　(i) $14x^2 - 28xy + 7y^2$
　　　　　　　　　　　　　(j) $-24b^2 + 56bc - 16c^2$

3　(a) $a^2 + 6a + 8$　(d) $12a^2 + 23a + 10$　(g) $18a^2 - 27ab + 4b^2$
　　(b) $b^2 - 4b + 3$　(e) $6z^2 + 10z - 24$　(h) $21m^2 + 2mn - 8n^2$
　　(c) $r^2 - 8r + 15$　(f) $10y^2 - 7yz - 12z^2$　(i) $24 + 24r + 6r^2$
　　　　　　　　　　　　　　(j) $36 + 24y - 12y^2$

4　(a) $3x - 2$　(d) $2ab + 3$　(g) $3 - 2b - b^2$
　　(b) $a - 3$　(e) $-2r - 1$　(h) $x^3y - 4x + 3y$
　　(c) $3x - 2$　(f) $-3a^2 + 2a - 4$

5　(a) $a + 2$　　(c) $x + 2$, rem. -6　(e) $x + 1$
　　(b) $3b + 3$　(d) $4r + 10$　　(f) $3m + 6n$

Exercise 5　Page 109

1　(a) $8a^2 + 6a$　(d) $12x - 6x^2$　(g) $2x - 4$
　　(b) $12r^2 - 24r$　(e) $6x^2y - 8xy^2$　(h) $8a + 10$
　　(c) $-42b - 21$　(f) $24t - 20t^2$

2　(a) $6a^3 + 21a^2 + 9a$　(d) $72r - 48r^2 - 36r^3$
　　(b) $20y^3 - 12y^2 - 48y$　(e) $8x^3y^3 - 6x^2y^2 - 8xy^3$
　　(c) $70x + 28x^2 - 7x^3$　(f) $-15p^3 + 18p^2 - 9p$

3　(a) $5a + 1$　(d) $-12y - 7$　(g) $11 - 8a$
　　(b) $6x^2 - 11x - 15$　(e) $6p + 9$　(h) $11c - 16$
　　(c) $b + 3$　(f) $x^2 + 2x + 9$　(i) $8x + 11$
　　　　　　　　　　　　(j) $2m + 2n$

13　Factors

Exercise 1　Page 111

1　(a) $8a^2 - 6$　　(c) $18x - 6x^2$　(e) $12a + 3a^2 - 6a^3$
　　(b) $3bc + 7b$　(d) $2x^2y - xy^2$　(f) $2a^2b + 2ab^2 - 2ab$
2　(a) $a + 2b$　(c) $a^2 + 1$　(e) $2x$
　　(b) $l + m$　(d) $1 - 5d$　(f) $-2a^2$

3 (a) $3x(2x+3)$ (d) $5(4p-3q)$ (g) $R(1-R)$
   (b) $4(x-2y)$ (e) $6x(x-2y)$ (h) $4b(b^2-2bc^2+3c)$
   (c) $a(a-4)$ (f) $3x^2(x-3y-2)$ (i) $3ab(a+2-3b)$
                                               (j) $2x^2(x^2-2x+1)$

4 (a) $(x+y)(z+2)$ (e) $(q+3r)(p-q)$
   (b) $2(a-2c)(b-2)$ (f) $(3+b)(2+a)$
   (c) $(a+d)(b-c)$ (g) $(x+3y)(2x-3)$
   (d) $(y+2)(2x+z)$

Exercise 2   Page 113

1 x^2+5x+6 **16** $5x^2+31x+6$ **31** $27+6s-s^2$
2 x^2+3x+2 **17** $6y^2+8y+2$ **32** $35+2p-p^2$
3 $a^2+9a+20$ **18** $15+21a+6a^2$ **33** $2a^2+8a-24$
4 $b^2+9b+20$ **19** $3+24c+21c^2$ **34** $12y^2-18y-12$
5 $m^2+8m+12$ **20** $50+40y+6y^2$ **35** $10x^2+44x-30$
6 $y^2+12y+35$ **21** $6a^2-16a+8$ **36** $24b^2+7b-5$
7 $12+7x+x^2$ **22** $6k^2-22k+20$ **37** $20+34a-12a^2$
8 $10+7a+a^2$ **23** $2b^2-17b+8$ **38** $8-22p-6p^2$
9 a^2-4a+3 **24** $6m^2-26m+24$ **39** $4y^2-4by+b^2$
10 $x^2-7x+10$ **25** $30-21a+3a^2$ **40** $9x^2-24x+16$
11 $z^2-10z+21$ **26** $35-43r+12r^2$ **41** $6r^2+rs-2s^2$
12 p^2-9p+8 **27** x^2+2x-8 **42** $3a^2-10ab-8b^2$
13 $15-8a+a^2$ **28** $x^2-4x-21$ **43** $2b^2+11cb-6c^2$
14 $24-10d+d^2$ **29** a^2-a-20 **44** $45x^2+17xy-6y^2$
15 $6x^2+13x+6$ **30** $b^2+9b-10$

Exercise 3   Page 116

1 $(x+2)(x+4)$ **8** $(b-3)(b-3)$ **15** $(a+12)(a-3)$
2 $(y+2)(y+5)$ **9** $(r-6)(r-2)$ **16** $(a+1)(a-3)$
3 $(a+3)(a+2)$ **10** $(s-5)(s-3)$ **17** $(x-6)(x+4)$
4 $(b+8)(b+1)$ **11** $(a+2)(a-1)$ **18** $(b-9)(b+3)$
5 $(x+5)(x+3)$ **12** $(x+3)(x-2)$ **19** $(y-5)(y+1)$
6 $(x-4)(x-2)$ **13** $(b+4)(b-2)$ **20** $(n-9)(n+1)$
7 $(a-2)(a-1)$ **14** $(t+6)(t-4)$

Exercise 4   Page 117

1 $(2x+4)(x+2)$ **6** $(2x-4)(x+3)$ **11** $(2a-b)(a-2b)$
2 $(3a+3)(a+2)$ **7** $(2r-1)(r-4)$ **12** $(2p-q)(p+q)$
3 $(2x+4)(x-5)$ **8** $(3s-4)(2s-2)$ **13** $(3-x)(2-2x)$
4 $(2b+4)(b-3)$ **9** $(2c+3)(c+1)$ **14** $(2-y)(3+3y)$
5 $(3y-6)(y+3)$ **10** $(2z+y)(z-y)$ **15** $(2+3a)(1-2a)$

Exercise 5   Page 119

1	x^2+6x+9	**15**	$(x-2)^2$	**29**	$(y^2-2z^2)(y^2+2z^2)$
2	$4x^2+20x+25$	**16**	$(2a-3)^2$	**30**	$(2x^2-11)(2x^2+11)$
3	$9a^2+12a+4$	**17**	$(p+2q)^2$	**31**	225
4	x^2-4x+4	**18**	$(2m-n)^2$	**32**	300
5	$9a^2-24a+16$	**19**	$(x-y)(x+y)$	**33**	624
6	$16c^2-24c+9$	**20**	$(2a-3b)(2a+3b)$	**34**	6,160
7	$4b^2+12bc+9c^2$	**21**	$(b-4)(b+4)$	**35**	2,907
8	$9x^2-24xy+16y^2$	**22**	$(a-1)(a+1)$	**36**	30,940
9	$16p^2-16pq+4q^2$	**23**	$(2-b)(2-b)$	**37**	14·91
10	$16c^2+56cd+49d^2$	**24**	$(x^2+10)(x^2-10)$	**38**	41·28
11	$16+16r+4r^2$	**25**	$(2p-3q)(2p+3q)$	**39**	127·05
12	$9-24k+16k^2$	**26**	$(6-4a)(6+4a)$	**40**	5
13	$(x+y)^2$	**27**	$(3ab-5)(3ab+5)$	**41**	10
14	$(3a+3b)^2$	**28**	$(7-6k)(7+6k)$		

14 Algebraic Fractions

Exercise 1   Page 121

1 (a) 10   (b) 49   (c) 30   (d) $4a$ (e) $20x$ (f) $12c^2$

2 (a) 16   (b) $5y$ (c) $3xy$ (d) $5cd$ (e) $y(x-2y)$ (f) $2r^2$

3 (a) $\dfrac{5}{7}$ (b) $\dfrac{7}{9}$ (c) $\dfrac{x}{4}$ (d) $\dfrac{1}{3}$

(e) $\dfrac{2}{3a}$ (f) $3x$ (g) $\dfrac{1}{3}$ (h) $\dfrac{1}{3c}$

(i) $\dfrac{2}{3r}$ (j) $a-b$ (k) $\dfrac{a+b}{4}$

Exercise 2   Page 123

1 (a) $1\frac{5}{12}$ (b) $\dfrac{5x}{6}$ (c) $\dfrac{5a}{4}$ (d) $\dfrac{21y}{10}$

2 (a) $\dfrac{13}{2b}$ (b) $\dfrac{10}{3x}$ (c) $\dfrac{a^2+6b}{3a}$ (d) $\dfrac{2x+z}{y}$

3 (a) $\dfrac{3}{8}$ (b) $\dfrac{x}{6}$ (c) $\dfrac{3p}{10}$ (d) $\dfrac{7n}{6}$

4 (a) $\dfrac{11}{2b}$ (b) $\dfrac{x(8y-3)}{6y}$ (c) $\dfrac{2a^2-b^2}{ab}$ (d) $\dfrac{9x^2-20y^2}{5xy}$

5 (a) $\dfrac{38x+27y}{12}$ (b) $\dfrac{x+12}{3}$ (c) $\dfrac{10x+4}{5x}$

6 (a) $\dfrac{5x+4y+10z}{20}$ (b) $\dfrac{x}{2}$ (c) $\dfrac{2b+c+12}{6}$

7 (a) $\dfrac{3+2c+3c^2}{c^2}$ (b) $\dfrac{3x}{8}$ (c) $\dfrac{7a}{12}$

8 (a) $\dfrac{3-2x+4x^2}{x^2}$ (b) $\dfrac{5ab-b+3a}{ab}$ (c) $\dfrac{15xy-3x^2+2y^2}{12xy}$

9 (a) $\dfrac{5c^2-2c-2}{c^2}$ (b) $\dfrac{36a-3b-2c}{12}$ (c) $\dfrac{2pqr+r-q}{qr}$

10 (a) $\dfrac{6a-3}{a}$ (b) $\dfrac{x-2y}{x-2}$

11 (a) $\dfrac{7b-4}{6}$ (b) $\dfrac{3r-20}{8}$

12 (a) $\dfrac{2x-3}{x+2}$ (b) $\dfrac{2p^2-5pq-10q}{p(p+2)}$

13 (a) $\dfrac{2(S-2)}{3}$ (b) $\dfrac{3b^2+2b-c^2+c}{bc}$

14 (a) $\dfrac{8a-d+15}{4(d-3)}$ (b) $\dfrac{22a-3}{3a}$

15 (a) $\dfrac{12c+6+c^2}{6c}$ (b) $\dfrac{40p-5q-2r}{10}$

Exercise 3   Page 126

1 (a) $\frac{5}{12}$ (b) $3\frac{1}{2}$ (c) $\dfrac{3a}{10}$ (d) $\dfrac{5x}{24}$

2 (a) $\dfrac{3y}{2}$ (b) $\dfrac{7y}{3}$ (c) $4pq$ (d) $\dfrac{a}{2b}$

3 (a) $\dfrac{x}{6}$ (b) $\frac{4}{5}$ (c) $\dfrac{xz}{y}$ (d) $6c$

4 (a) $\dfrac{2(2x+3)}{3(2x-3)}$ (b) $\dfrac{a}{a+3}$ (c) $\dfrac{2b-6}{b+3}$

5 (a) $\dfrac{2}{3ab}$ (b) $\dfrac{3c(4c+1)}{5(4c-1)}$ (c) $\dfrac{4a^2+4a}{a-2}$

6 (a) $1\frac{7}{25}$ (b) $\frac{11}{54}$ (c) $\dfrac{6a}{5}$ (d) $\dfrac{2x}{3}$

7 (a) $\dfrac{15}{2y}$ (b) $1\frac{1}{2}$ (c) $\dfrac{2y}{x}$ (d) $\dfrac{9pq}{10r^2}$

8 (a) $\dfrac{a}{2(a+b)}$ (b) $\dfrac{x-2y}{z(x+4y)}$ (c) $\dfrac{3a}{2}$ (d) $12r^5$

9 (a) $b(a-2)$ (b) $\dfrac{2a(3a-2b)}{a+b}$ (c) $\dfrac{2b}{9c}$ (d) $\dfrac{x+y}{2x}$

10 (a) $\dfrac{2c^2}{3bd}$ (b) $\dfrac{x}{y}$ (c) $\dfrac{3a(a-b)}{2b(a+b)}$

15 Simple Equations

Exercise 1   Page 131

1 $x = 24$

2 (a) $x = 25$ (b) $x = 6$ (c) $a = 19$
    (d) $b = 3$ (e) $c = 36$ (f) $d = 7$

3 (a) $x = 6$ (b) $b = 6$ (c) $y = 9$
    (d) $c = \frac{1}{2}$ (e) $x = \frac{1}{2}$ (f) $b = \frac{1}{4}$

4 (a) $c = 25$ (b) $x = 64$ (c) $d = 32$
    (d) $a = 9$ (e) $x = 12$ (f) $b = 7$

5 (a) $x = 3$ (b) $a = 4$ (c) $y = 6$
    (d) $a = 3$ (e) $c = 3$ (f) $b = 1\frac{3}{5}$

6 (a) $x = 5$ (b) $y = 4$ (c) $b = 3$
    (d) $a = 5$ (e) $r = 15$ (f) $c = 6$

7 (a) $x = -5$ (b) $y = -4$ (c) $a = 11$
    (d) $z = -8$ (e) $c = -2$ (f) $b = -4$

8 (a) $a = 4$ (b) $x = -5$ (c) $n = 6$
    (d) $y = 5$ (e) $r = 4$ (f) $x = 18$

Exercise 2   Page 134

1 (a) $x = 2$ (b) $a = 1$ (c) $b = 3$
    (d) $x = 2$ (e) $b = 3$ (f) $a = -7$

2 (a) $b = -2$ (b) $x = -2\frac{7}{8}$ (c) $x = 11$ (d) $c = \frac{6}{7}$

3 (a) $a = 2$ (b) $d = 1\frac{1}{5}$ (c) $x = 4\frac{1}{6}$ (d) $P = 8$
    (e) $a = 10$ (f) $z = 0.84$ (g) $y = 14$ (h) $x = 16$

4 (a) $y = -26$ (b) $a = -11$ (c) $x = 5$
    (d) $b = 5$ (e) $z = 0$ (f) $x = -15$

5 (a) $x = 55$ (b) $a = 16$ (c) $z = 12$
    (d) $a = 18$ (e) $n = 4$ (f) $x = 5$

6 (a) $a = 4$ (b) $x = 21$ (c) $c = \frac{1}{3}$
    (d) $b = -1\frac{1}{5}$ (e) $a = -1\frac{1}{5}$ (f) $y = -12$

Exercise 3   Page 137

1 (a) 9   (b) 36   (c) 12

2 14, 16   **3** 7, 9, 11   **4** 6, 5   **5** 12 m, 7 m

6 $x = 40$, $\angle A = 30°$, $\angle B = 80°$, $\angle C = 70°$

7 15 litres grade 1, 20 litres grade 2
8 (a) 4 km/h   (b) 40 km/h   **9** 11
10 YX 6 cm, XZ 3 cm, YZ 5 cm   **11** £3, £4, £5   **12** 28

16 Formulae

Exercise 1   Page 138

1 (i) A $= xy$ cm^2 (ii) Wt. $= \dfrac{xy}{250}$ kg

2 V $= abc$ cm^3, C $= \dfrac{abc}{1000}$ litres

3 $\angle X = 180° - (\angle Y + \angle Z)$

4 (i) $2S$ km   (ii) $7S$ km   (iii) St km

5 (i) $\dfrac{S}{60}$ km/min   (ii) $\dfrac{50S}{3}$ m/min

6 (i) £ $\dfrac{7l}{100}$ (ii) £ $\dfrac{ly}{100}$ **7** lhp pence, £ $\dfrac{lhp}{100}$

8 (i) $\dfrac{11x^2}{14}$ cm^2 (ii) $\dfrac{33x^2}{14}$ cm^2 **9** $\dfrac{k}{l}$

10 $2(a+b)$ cm, $\dfrac{(a+b)}{50}$ m   **11** $\dfrac{3d}{100}$ metres, $\dfrac{d^2\sqrt{3}}{4}$ cm^2

12 $a^2 - \pi r^2$

Exercise 2   Page 142

1 (a) 80·6 cm^2 (b) $\dfrac{A}{b} = h$, 11·6 cm

2 (i) $h = \dfrac{V}{lb}$ (ii) $1\frac{1}{2}$ m   **6** (i) $u = V - at$ (ii) $t = \dfrac{V-u}{a}$

3 $d = \dfrac{C}{\pi}$ **7** $P = 15 - \dfrac{3q}{4}$

4 $V = \dfrac{k}{P}$ **8** $r = \sqrt{R^2 - \dfrac{A}{\pi}}$ or $\sqrt{\dfrac{\pi R^2 - A}{\pi}}$

5 $V = 2S - U$ **9** $R = \dfrac{u^2}{32}$; R $= 50$

10 (i) $P = \dfrac{100I}{RT}$ (ii) $R = \dfrac{100I}{PT}$ (iii) $T = \dfrac{100I}{PR}$

11 (i) £200   (ii) 4 yr

17 Simultaneous and Quadratic Equations

Exercise 1   Page 146

1 $x = 4, y = 6$	**11** $x = 2, y = 4$	**21** $x = 5, y = 2$
2 $x = 2, y = 8$	**12** $x = 3, y = 1$	**22** $x = 2, y = 3$
3 $x = 4, y = 2$	**13** $a = 3, b = 1\frac{1}{2}$	**23** $a = -2, b = 1$
4 $a = 11, b = 7$	**14** $a = 4, b = -3$	**24** $p = 2, q = 1\frac{1}{2}$
5 $a = -30, b = -12$	**15** $x = 2, y = 1$	**25** $b = 9, c = 4$
6 $a = 8, y = 19$	**16** $x = 3, y = 2$	**26** $m = 2, n = 1\frac{1}{2}$
7 $b = 10, c = -4$	**17** $x = 2, y = 2$	**27** $a = 7\frac{1}{5}, b = 7\frac{1}{5}$
8 $x = 2, y = 1$	**18** $a = 1, b = \frac{1}{5}$	**28** $a = -1, b = -2$
9 $x = 7, y = 1$	**19** $x = 3, y = 6$	**29** $a = 4, b = 3$
10 $x = 6, y = 2$	**20** $a = 9\frac{1}{2}, y = 2$	**30** $P = 18, q = 2$

Exercise 2   Page 149

1 $5, 2$	**8** $3, 2$	**15** $-\frac{2}{3}, 1\frac{1}{2}$
2 $9, -7$	**9** $3, -2$	**16** $-3, 2$
3 $-2, 3$	**10** $-4, 1$	**17** $2, 1$
4 4	**11** $4, -2$	**18** $0, 2\frac{1}{2}$
5 $-5, -2$	**12** $3, 4$	**19** $1\frac{1}{2}, -1\frac{1}{2}$
6 $-\frac{1}{4}, 1$	**13** $1\frac{1}{2}, -2$	**20** $0, 3$
7 $3, -3$	**14** $-1, 2$	

PART THREE—GRAPHS

18 Charts and Diagrams

Exercise 1   Page 154

1 *(a)* Approx. 2·5 cm to 1 hour
   (b) Copenhagen 976 km   Dusseldorf 712 km
       Zurich   920 km   Brussels   589 km
       Frankfurt   848 km   Amsterdam 515 km
2 40 to 50
5 *(a)* July or August   *(b)* January or December   *(c)* No

Exercise 2   Page 160

1 *(a)* 24, 54, 103·20, 157·20
   (b) £6·25, £10·41½, £21·04, £29·17
2 *(a)* 60·30 fc, 6·70 fc, 50·25 fc, 670 fc
   (b) £0·71, £4·10, £1·28½, £3·17
3 *(a)* 2·78 m/s, 4·17 m/s, 6·95 m/s
   (b) 10·8 km/h, 23·4 km/h, 18·9 km/h
4 *(a)* (i) 43·75 km   (ii) 23·3 km
   (b) (i) 11·25 km   (ii) 6 km
   (c) (i) 13·6 min   (ii) 25·5 min
5 (i) 12½p   (ii) 69p to nearest penny   (iii) £2·12½
6 *(a)* (i) 10·5 cm (ii) 3·8 cm   *(b)* (i) 22 cm (ii) 17·6 cm
7 10·24 hours
8 *(a)* 192 km   *(b)* Smith 69 km, Jones 192 km
   (c) Smith 13·8 km/h, Jones 38·4 km/h
   (d) $\frac{111}{150}$, $\frac{13}{40}$; 74 km/h, 19·5 km/h
   (e) 0, 0, no gradient
   (f) 30 min, 60 min. Both stopped   *(g)* 50 km

19 Graphs with Positive and Negative Values

Exercise 1   Page 168

1 *(a)* x values: $-\frac{2}{3}$, $\frac{2}{3}$, 3, $-2\cdot13$
   (b) y values: 3½, -1, $-3\cdot25$, $-1\cdot9$
2 *(a)* $(-4, -3)$, $(2\cdot5, -1\cdot5)$, $(-2, 2)$, $(2\cdot5, 0)$, $(0, 3\cdot5)$
   (b) $(-2, -4)$, $(1, 0\cdot6)$

3   $y = -7, -4, -1, 2, 5, 8$
    $x = 1.8, y = -5.5, x = 0.7, y = 6.2, y = 1.25$
7   $x = 4, y = 2$ 8 $x = -1\frac{1}{2}, y = 3\frac{1}{2}$ 9 $x = 18, y = 2$

20 Curved Graphs

Exercise 1   Page 174

1   *(a)* 06·29   *(b)* 07·20$\frac{1}{2}$ *(c)* 08·04

2

Angle	10°	22°	31°	39°	45°	58°	64°	76°
Length of Tangent in mm	6·6	15	22·5	30·4	37·5	60	76·8	150·4

    (a) 10·1 mm, 17·6 mm, 26·25 mm, 115·4 mm
    (b) 7° 36′, 13° 30′, 35° 21′
3   *(a)* 30·625 m   *(b)* 24·5 m
4   1·1 amps, 10 volts
5   10 cm², 174·3 cm², 19·4 cm²

21 Lines and Angles

Exercise 1 Page 177

1. $\angle$a = 73°; $\angle b$ = 107°; $\angle c$ = 73°
2. $\angle a$ = 150°; $\angle b$ = 135°   3 $\angle a$ = 113°
4. (i) 60°   (ii) 36°   (iii) 30°   (iv) 45°
5. $\angle x$ = 60°; $\angle a$ = 120°; $\angle b$ = 60°
6. $\angle x$ = 30°; $\angle a$ = 120°; $\angle b$ = 60°
7. $\angle x$ = 20°; $\angle$s a, b, c = 60°   8 60°
9. 70°   10 110°   11 100°   12 75°
13. No   14 Yes   15 Yes   16 Yes

22 Bearings

Exercise 1 Page 180

1. A = N 30°E, 030°   B = N 50°E, 050°   C = N 60°E, 060°
   D = S 50°E, 130°   E = S 20°E, 160°   F = S 45°W, 225°
   G = N 70°W, 290°   H = N 45°W, 315°
2. 335°, 170°, 026°, 256°,   3 N5°E, N84°W, E(N90°E), S13°W
4. (i) 110°, 095°   (ii) 135°, 110°   BC is parallel to AD
5. 307°; 100 km   6 283°; 7·5 km

23 Angles of Triangles, Quadrilaterals and Polygons

Exercise 1 Page 187

1. $\angle$x = 30°, $\angle$y = 36°, $\angle$z = 33°, $\angle$a = 154°, $\angle$b = 90°,
   $\angle$m = 140°, $\angle$n = 15°
2. $\angle$p = 45°, $\angle$q = 98°, $\angle$r = 60°, $\angle$s = 114°, $\angle$v = 70°,
   $\angle$w = 40°
3. $\angle$s = 40°, $\angle$t = 40°; $\angle$x = 70°, $\angle$y = 140°; $\angle$w, v, x, y = 35°; $\angle$a = 95°, $\angle$b = 80°

24 Constructions

Exercise 1 Page 196

1. XZ = 8·66 cm, ZY = 4·33 cm, $\angle$Z = 60°
2. CB = 5·7 cm, $\angle$C = 96°, $\angle$B = 39°   4 TQ = 2 cm
5. FH = 2·25 cm, HE = 2·25 cm, GH = 3·45 cm, HD = 3·45 cm   6 $\angle$B = 90°, 28 mm

25 Congruent Triangles

Exercise 1   Page 199

1 Fig. 107, congruent, A.S.A.   Fig. 110, congruent, S.S.S.
  Fig. 108, congruent, A.S.A.   Fig. 111, not congruent
  Fig. 109, not congruent
2 *(a)* Not congruent *(b)* Congruent, A.S.A. *(c)* Not congruent *(d)* Congruent, S.S.A. *(e)* Not congruent

Exercise 2   Page 202

4 $\angle PQS = 55°$

26 Parallelograms

Exercise 1   Page 210

2 AD = 7·5 cm, DM = 7·5 cm, $\angle D = 110°$, $\angle DMA = 35°$
3 US = 10 cm, UT = 10 cm, ST = 9 cm
10 $\angle A = 105°$, $\angle B = 75°$, $\angle C = 105°$, $\angle D = 75°$

27 Pythagoras' Theorem

Exercise 1   Page 218

1 Right-angled: *(a)* $\angle BAC$, *(b)* $\angle BAC$, *(d)* $\angle XZY$, *(e)* $\angle QPR$; not right-angled: *(c)*
2 *(a)* 17 cm *(b)* 1·2 m *(c)* 35 cm *(d)* 29 m
3 12·2 cm **4** 8·9 m **5** 70·7 mm **6** 7·07 m
7 5·4 cm **8** 53 m **10** 250 mm

28 Similar Triangles

Exercise 1   Page 224

1 (i) $x = 4$ cm, $y = 6$ cm (ii) $x = 3·75$ cm, $y = 1·5$ cm
  (iii) $x = 0·45$ m, $y = 0·9$ m
2 $\dfrac{AB}{DE} = \dfrac{5}{10}$, $\dfrac{AC}{DF} = \dfrac{4\frac{1}{2}}{9}$
3 AE = 6 cm, CE = 10 cm **4** 25·28 m
5 DF = 10 cm, AB = 4 cm, AC = 3 cm
6 (i) 1·1, 1·2, 0·7 (ii) 1·1, 1·2, 0·7
7 $\dfrac{RP}{TS} = \dfrac{1}{3}$, TS = 2·4 m **8** PT = 2·4 cm, TS = 4·8 cm
9 AE 40 m, OD 12 m **10** (i) 12 m (ii) 4 m
11 RS 8 cm, RT 10 cm **12** FG 20 cm, EG 36·06 cm

29 The Circle

Exercise 1   Page 233

1 (i) AE   (ii) $\angle$EAD, $\angle$EBD, $\angle$ECD   (iii) $\angle$CBD, $\angle$CED
2 (i) 42°   (ii) 65°   (iii) 60°   (iv) 65°   (v) 75°   (vi) 122°
3 (i) 110°   (ii) 59°   (iii) 70°   (iv) 38°
4 50°   **5** 60°   **6** 178°   **7** 25°   **8** $\angle x = 50°$; $\angle y = 55°$
9 110°

Exercise 2   Page 240

1 6 cm   **2** 3 cm   **3** 7·4 cm   **4** 21·46 cm   **6** 22·36 cm

Exercise 3   Page 242

1 70°   **2** 60°   **3** 75°   **4** 80°   **5** 100°   **6** 55°
7 (i) 35°   (ii) 90°   (iii) 60°   **8** (i) 50°   (ii) 60°

PART FIVE—LOGARITHMS, SQUARES, SQUARE ROOTS FROM TABLES, TRIGONOMETRY

32 Logarithms and Anti-logarithms

Exercise 1   Page 252

1 $52 = 10^{1\cdot716}$; $5\cdot25 = 10^{0\cdot7202}$; $546 = 10^{2\cdot7372}$;
$53\cdot67 = 10^{1\cdot7298}$; $5,345 = 10^{3\cdot7279}$; $51,240 = 10^{4\cdot7096}$;
$5\cdot026 = 10^{0\cdot7012}$

2   *(a)* 0·7115, 1·7115, 2·7115, 3·7115
   (b) 1·7306, 0·7175, 0·7025, 2·7372
   (c) 4·7190, 0·7061, 2·7386, 1·7109

3   *(a)* 0·9191   *(b)* 2·9191   *(c)* 3·9191

4   *(a)* 1·2417   *(b)* 3·2417   *(c)* 2·2417

Exercise 2   Page 254

1   42·1, 43·72, 4·293, 4·298

2   4,316, 398·2, 4·445, 444·3

3   2,933, 29·33, 293·3

4   *(a)* 0·8727   *(d)* 2·7463   *(g)* 1·9542
   (b) 1·6163   *(e)* 3·7782   *(h)* 2·5348
   (c) 0·9033   *(f)* 2·3572   *(i)* 5·3979

5   *(a)* 22·21   *(d)* 5,571   *(g)* 32,910
   (b) 1·176   *(e)* 250   *(h)* 18·61
   (c) 179·7   *(f)* 9·074   *(i)* 2,075

33 More Work with Logarithms

Exercise 1   Page 257

1   *(a)* $\bar{1}$·4393   *(d)* $\bar{4}$·1461   *(g)* $\bar{1}$·4191
   (b) $\bar{3}$·8344   *(e)* $\bar{1}$·6592   *(h)* $\bar{3}$·6385
   (c) $\bar{2}$·4871   *(f)* $\bar{1}$·5761   *(i)* $\bar{2}$·9229

2   *(a)* 0·4307   *(d)* 0·006551   *(g)* 0·1586
   (b) 0·02478   *(e)* 0·0001296   *(h)* 0·003677
   (c) 0·4307   *(f)* 0·06088   *(i)* 0·0002994

Exercise 2   Page 259

1	11·41	**7**	5·646	**13**	10·05
2	132·4	**8**	6·627	**14**	3·029
3	702·8	**9**	2·001	**15**	395·9
4	3·565	**10**	3·413	**16**	0·8586
5	0·02993	**11**	69·63	**17**	2·606
6	0·05644	**12**	0·005384		

Exercise 3   Page 261

1	28·3	**9**	0·01129	**16**	0·8976
2	641·8	**10**	3·105	**17**	0·3719
3	191·4	**11**	9·817	**18**	0·463
4	904	**12**	4·019	**19**	1·91
5	0·6561	**13**	6·981	**20**	1·209
6	0·0003215	**14**	0·8555	**21**	2·472
7	0·1681	**15**	0·2269	**22**	273·3
8	0·00002364				

Exercise 4   Page 263

1	68·9	**5**	1,420 cm^2	**8**	1·18
2	3·50	**6**	4·47	**9**	0·045
3	273	**7**	69·3	**10**	9·92
4	0·640				

34 Squares of Numbers from Tables

Exercise 1   Page 266

1	(a) 441	(d) 4·41	(g) 0·0441
	(b) 576	(e) 5·76	(h) 0·0576
	(c) 784	(f) 7·84	(i) 0·0784
2	(a) 506·3	(d) 0·0841	(g) 0·00000529
	(b) 7·513	(e) 0·06452	(h) 0·0006812
	(c) 429·7	(f) 0·07155	(i) 0·0005655
3	(a) 15,630	(d) 384·2	(g) 1046
	(b) 306·3	(e) 222	(h) 1·96
	(c) 3102	(f) 447·8	(i) 130
4	(a) 59·77	(e) 0·00004096	(i) 0·00001849
	(b) 0·003982	(f) 27·57	(j) 0·03063
	(c) 0·001867	(g) 508·1	(k) 1401
	(d) 0·01166	(h) 92·74	(l) 0·003295

35 Square Roots from Tables

Exercise 1   Page 269

1	*(a)* 7	*(e)*	0·6633	*(i)*	0·6595
	(b) 2·214	*(f)*	0·06928	*(j)*	0·2049
	(c) 2·012	*(g)*	0·6812	*(k)*	0·0645
	(d) 20·12	*(h)*	2·198	*(l)*	0·06921
2	*(a)* 8	*(d)*	2·53	*(g)*	0·8
	(b) 12	*(e)*	3·795	*(h)*	0·12
	(c) 25	*(f)*	2·5	*(i)*	0·07906
3	*(a)* 5·851	*(e)*	9·2	*(i)*	0·86
	(b) 7·533	*(f)*	3·095	*(j)*	0·021
	(c) 2·584	*(g)*	36·64	*(k)*	0·91
	(d) 2·785	*(h)*	0·52	*(l)*	0·23
4	*(a)* 75·16	*(e)*	1·065	*(i)*	2·477
	(b) 6·069	*(f)*	0·272	*(j)*	4·034
	(c) 1·623	*(g)*	0·2902	*(k)*	0·5699
	(d) 0·08313	*(h)*	48·37	*(l)*	15·8

36 Trigonometry

Exercise 1   Page 276

2 10°, 25°, 40°, 55°, 75°

3 (i) $\dfrac{RP}{QP}$ (ii) $\dfrac{XY}{ZX}$

4 (i) $\angle C$ (ii) $\angle R$ (iii) $\angle Y$

5 75·1 mm   **10** 72°   **15** 5·3 m

6 16·4 cm   **11** 26 m   **16** 32°, 58°

7 14°   **12** 76°   **17** 4·5 cm

8 22·7 cm   **13** 75 m   **18** (i) 69·5 m   (ii) 394·2 m

9 28·6 cm   **14** 4·9 m   **19** 1·6 cm, 5·6 cm^2

Exercise 2   Page 279

3 *(a)* 0·1392, 0·2588, 0·5, 0·6293, 0·7071, 0·9659, 0·9925
   (b) 0·9903, 0·9659, 0·866, 0·7771, 0·7071, 0·2588, 0·1219

4 12°, 23°, 40°, 55°, 82°

5 10°, 44°, 60°, 80°, 70°

6 (i) $\dfrac{AC}{BC}$ (ii) $\dfrac{BA}{BC}$ (iii) $\dfrac{PR}{QR}$ (iv) $\dfrac{ZX}{ZY}$ (v) $\dfrac{RP}{RQ}$

   (vi) $\dfrac{AB}{AC}$ (vii) $\dfrac{PQ}{RQ}$ (viii) $\dfrac{YX}{YZ}$ (ix) $\dfrac{XZ}{YX}$ (x) $\dfrac{XY}{YZ}$

Exercise 3　Page 281

1	AB 102·4 mm, BC 71·7 mm	**5**	106 m
2	55°, to nearest degree	**6**	0·835 m²
3	2·9 m	**7**	8·38 cm, 5·44 cm
4	8°	**8**	1·732 km

Exercise 4　Page 284

1

	145°	180°	85°	160°	98°
Sin	0·5736	0	0·9962	0·3420	0·9903
Cos	−0·8192	−1	0·0872	−0·9397	−0·1392
Tan	−0·7002	0	11·43	−0·3640	−7·1154

2 81·19 cm²　**3** 5·72 cm²　**4** 22·1 m²　**5** 1·133 km²
6 66·5 cm²　**7** 25·4 cm², 4·93 cm, 21° (21° 33′)
8 ∠ACB = 108°

Exercise 5　Page 287

2 0·7986　**3** 21° 48′　**4** DE = 32·47, DF = 18·75 cm
5 XZ = 20 cm, ∠Y = 53°, ∠Z = 37°　**6** 96·5 m
7 *(a)* 46·6 m　*(b)* 32·6 m　**8** 120·7 m
9 AB = 1,912 km, CD = 1,345 km, AD = BC = 3,350 km
10 *(a)* T is 558·2 km north of P
　　(b) Madrid to Philadelphia 6,074 km

PART SIX—MISCELLANEOUS EXERCISES

37 Miscellaneous Short Questions

Page 291

1	$7\frac{1}{2}$p	**17**	$\frac{3}{8}, \frac{5}{16}, \frac{7}{24}, \frac{9}{32}, \frac{1}{4}$
2	23	**18**	270
3	2·6	**19**	*(a)* 6·753 *(b)* 0·5138
4	£1·40, £2·45	**20**	$t = 5$
5	$5a(3a + 1)$	**21**	Yes. $\angle$ABC
6	£49·50	**22**	0·212 m
7	0·0555	**23**	$\angle$BCD = 55°
8	3^4		$\angle$ABD = 55°
9	0·65		$\angle$ADB = 100°
10	$\frac{3}{4}$	**24**	0·6
11	18	**25**	*(a)* 26·03 *(b)* 26·03
12	$8a^3b - 6ab^2$		*(c)* 2230_5
13	(i) $(3x + 5y)(3x - 5y)$	**26**	-2 or 1
	(ii) $\pi(R + r)(R - r)$	**27**	£15·37$\frac{1}{2}$
14	2,740	**28**	103
15	£16·25	**29**	(i) 3 (ii) 1 (iii) 9
16	2, 11, 23, 26	**30**	-12

38 Miscellaneous Problems

Page 293

1	5,933	**10**	708; 413 boys
2	6,909	**11**	20,484; 6,276; 2,466
3	7·7 t	**12**	137,066; 3,951
4	£455 p.a. by £2·60	**13**	£14·02$\frac{1}{2}$
5	$8\frac{1}{2}$ h; £2·29$\frac{1}{2}$	**14**	3
6	709 tonnes	**15**	£13·06
7	(i) £30 (ii) £1,200 (iii) $\frac{1}{2}$	**16**	6·19$\frac{1}{2}$ p.m.
8	£4·76; 12·2 m	**17**	134·75 kg
9	£82,325	**18**	(i) 10·92 t (ii) £98·28

19 (i) 54,750   (ii) 11,315
        (iii) 59,130 m³
20 90 m, 10 rolls
21 26, 70·2 m, 9 rolls
22 500 r.p.m.
23 $\frac{3}{4}$
24 $1\frac{1}{3}$
25 0·15 m³
26 1,944, 243 kg
27 £7·10
28 £2·82
29 374
30 3 mm
31 0·6875, $\frac{1}{8}$
32 $\frac{3}{4}$, $3\frac{1}{8}$, $1\frac{19}{20}$, $2\frac{5}{8}$, $4\frac{9}{16}$
33 16 m, 57·6 km/h
34 *(a)* £176·6   *(b)* £1,766
        (c) £17,660
35 £3·64
36 £4·48
37 A 585 km, B 562·5 km
38 2·13
39 £11·74$\frac{1}{2}$
40 £22·50
41 18·9 m
42 50 kg
43 *(a)* 488   *(b)* 502   *(c)* 27
44 87·5 kg
45 113·04
46 2 cm²
47 $18x^2 - 22z + 6y$
48 (i) $2x^2 + 7x - 30$
        (ii) -20
49 (i) 7 cm (ii) 10 cm (iii) 3 cm
50 805 g
51 60%
52 CA = 4·2 cm, YZ = 9 cm
53 16 cm, 20 cm, 90°
54 $x = 4$, $y = -1$
55 110°

56 (i) $x = 3$ (ii) $z = 8$
        (iii) $x = 5\frac{2}{3}$
57 7, 9, 11
58 18°, 54°, 108°
59 £7·09, 28·6%
60 ACB = 120°, ACB = 60°,
        ABO = 30°
61 1486·8 cm³
62 40°
63 378 litres
64 449·5 cm²
67 (i) $11a^2 + 6ab - 11b^2$
        (ii) $6a^2 - 13a + 6$
68 (i) $(4a + 5)(4a - 5)$
        (ii) $(3b + c)(3b - c)$
        (iii) $a^3(2 + 3a)(2 - 3a)$
69 12 years
70 3·5 m
71 (i) $\frac{1}{20,000}$ (ii) 16·6 m/s
72 64 km/h
73 51·96 m
75 (i) £9·19 (to nearest penny)
        (ii) £450
76 4·625 m³
77 1·1 m³, 1,100 litres
78 £96·36$\frac{1}{2}$
79 $a = 32°$, $x = 30°$
80 (a) $3a^3 - 4a^2 - 8a + 8$
        (b) $a^2 - 2a + 1$
82 $\dfrac{500Vt}{3}$
83 (i) $(c + 5)(c - 5)$
        (ii) $(2a + 8)(2a - 8)$
        (iii) $(9 + 3x)(9 - 3x)$
84 (i) 1,400   (ii) 3,600
        (iii) 2,800   (iii) 1,520
85 £100
86 60%
87 1312·5 t

88 (*a*) (i) 14°C   (ii) 14°C
     (*b*) (i) 6°C   (ii) 8°C
     (*c*) 10°C, 20°C
89 170, 41·6 km
90 (*a*) 45°   (*b*) 36°
91 20
92 (i) 72 litres   (ii) 0·25 m
93 (i) $(x-3)(x-2)$
    (ii) $(1+3x)(1-x)$
    (iii) $(2x+1)(x+3)$
94 125°
95 $2\frac{1}{2}$ years
96 AD = 5·55 cm
    BD = 5·55 cm
    CD = 4·4 cm
97 50
98 £1·80
99 121·5 kg
101 3 km, 08·39
102 (i) 8·34   (ii) 5·47
     (iii) 14·7
103 6·9 cm
104 34·6 m
105 42·2 m², ·7912 m³
106 (*a*) 7 kg   (*b*) £55·90
107 (*a*) (i) 331   (ii) $\frac{11}{20}$
        (iii) 84
     (*b*) (i) 60   (ii) 900
108 Maths. 55·3, Eng. 46·4
109 (*a*) 12·5   (*b*) 0·63
     (*c*) 9·53
110 (*a*) 15 mm   (*b*) 12 cm
     (*c*) 3·21 m
111 (*a*) $x = 2\frac{4}{5}$, $y = -\frac{1}{5}$
     (*b*) $x = 4$, $y = 3$
112 1766·25 cm³, 2:3 approx.
113 26 cm
114 5·4 m, 48°
115 (*a*) (i) 5·652 m²
         (ii) 169·56 m²
     (*b*) 6·5 cm

116 13·4 cm²
117 £9·11
118 (*a*) -2 (*b*) 23
120 93·6 m
121 263·3 cm
122 $\angle$BDE = 60°,
    $\angle$BOE = 120°
123 CD = 5·77 cm,
    DB = 2·8 cm
    36·9 cm²
124 0·107 m³
125 (*a*) 15°   (*b*) 166·7 mm
126 (*a*) (i) 8·35   (ii) 2·99
     (*b*) (i) $9·6 \times 10^7$
         (ii) $5·4 \times 10^{-4}$
127 11·55 (approx.)
128 130 mm
129 63·9 m
130 $L = \dfrac{P}{2} - W$, 8
131 295·2 m
132 (*a*) 1·16 m²   (*b*) 2 m²
133 (*a*) $\frac{3}{5}$ (*b*) 11·08 km
134 15 h, 20%
135 7,093 cm³ or 7·093 litres
136 32
137 £449·95
138 (i) 5, 2   (ii) $-7, -3$
     (iii) 0, -3
139 PR = 6·4, TP = 4·47 cm
141 (*a*) 52,752 km
     (*b*) 29,655 km/h
142 1·13 m², 70·9 litres
143 (i) 122·5 m
     (ii) 30·625 m, 4·5 s
144 $x = 5, y = 2$
145 (*a*) £3·90   (*b*) $12\frac{1}{2}$%
146 'A' £362·50, 'B', £483·33,
     'C', £604·16$\frac{1}{2}$
147 157 cm²

148   55·4 km

149   *(a)* $\frac{3}{7}$ *(b)* 5, 10

     (c) $\frac{1}{5}, \frac{2}{7}, \frac{2}{5}, \frac{2}{3}, \frac{3}{4}, \frac{5}{6}, \frac{6}{7}$

150   *(a)* $6,339_{12}$

     (b) $322, 536_{8}$

     (c) 1010110 rem. 101

151   *(a)* £2·95$\frac{1}{2}$ *(b)* £928·72

     (c) £5·36$\frac{1}{2}$

152   29° 30′ N